Never Play Leapfrog with a Unicorn

Also by David Kitchen

Axed Between The Ears
Earshot

Published by
Heinemann Educational Books

David Kitchen
illustrated by Nick Sharratt

Never play Leapfrog with a Unicorn

and other poems

mammoth

*for Gareth, Rhiannon
and Alison*

First published in Great Britain 1995
by Heinemann Young Books
Published 1997 by Mammoth
an imprint of Reed International Books Ltd
Michelin House, 81 Fulham Road, London SW3 6RB
and Auckland and Melbourne

ISBN 0 7497 1993 1

A CIP catalogue record for this title
is available from the British Library

Printed in Great Britain
by Cox & Wyman Ltd, Reading, Berkshire

Contents

I thought I wasn't here

From Septimus to Smith

Perfectly Peculiar

Say What You Think

I thought I wasn't Here

What, Miss?

Homework?
Did we have homework?

You was away on Monday, miss,
So we thought you'd be away today.

I've done it, miss
But I've left my book up my nan's.

I lent my book to Darren
And he's away today.

I've got my book, miss
But I did the work on paper
And I think I left it at home.

My baby sister
Got hold of all my books
And was sick on them.

I thought I had a dental appointment
This morning, miss
But it's this afternoon
So I've got the books for this afternoon
When I'll be at the dentist
But I haven't got this morning's books
Because I thought I wasn't here.

I had a brain relapse, miss.

Just Because You're New

When you get to high school,
Just because you're new,
They throw you down a twelve foot bank
And shove you down the loo.

Your head's kept there for half an hour
Until your breath gives out
But still they keep on flushing
Because no one's about.

The teachers are like skyscrapers,
Fog horns where mouths should be,
Their strength comes from the ground-up
  bones
Of those who disagree.

The railings round the school
Are ten feet high or more
And every year someone gets speared.
I think that's what they're for.

There's such a rush for dinners,
Don't bother. Get out of the way.
One girl got splatted flat as a mat:
You can see the mark to this day.

If you don't get crushed at dinner,
You'll get pulped by Room 48:
The lab is locked till teachers come
And teachers are always late.

You get detention for sniffing in class
Three hundred lines if you cough
And, just for fun, there's someone
Who will twist your neck till your head pops
    off.

There's chinese burns and armlocks,
There's holding you upside down.
You think it's bad? I tell you,
It's the quietest school in town!

Says . . . Means

Enjoys class discussion.
MEANS Shouts louder than everyone else.

Tries to be helpful.
MEANS Pesters teachers every two minutes
until they explode.

Needs to put a little more time into his work.
MEANS Hasn't brought a pen to school since
the third day of the term.

Has a very supportive family.
MEANS His father used to be in the Marines
and beats to pulp anyone who upsets his little boy.

Frequently late for morning registration.
MEANS Arrives in time for lunch.

*Frequently misses both morning and
afternoon registration.*
MEANS Arrives in time for lunch and goes
home immediately afterwards.

Could try harder.
MEANS Could bring his brain to school.

Produces the most interesting stories in the group.
MEANS Is a pathological liar.

Has a strong personality.
MEANS Hits the majority of children.

Has a very strong personality.
MEANS Hits the majority of teachers.

An unpredictable pupil.
MEANS When his best friend lent him a book to copy up, he burnt it on the way home.

Has not yet grasped all the implications of safety in education.
MEANS Is being summonsed for opening the emergency doors on the school bus and pushing five children off.

Nothing Much

A Yorkie's got stuck in the vending machine,
It needs to be sorted out now;
Darren took Tina clubbing last night
So Debbie has called her a cow.

That's because Debbie likes Darren a lot,
Although she's been going with Wayne;
The man with the leaflets about student
  rights
Is out by the school gates again.

When the Head gets to hear, he'll be down
  to the gate
And poking the bloke in the chest;
Going by past behaviour and style,
The head is the one they'll arrest.

The drama department is doing a play
With language not fit for a sewer,
Barbara's mum is demanding a ban
Because, she says, Barbara is pure.

Mum doesn't know of the end of term dance,
The French trip or Valentine party.
Barbara may be angelic at home;
Outside she's incurably tarty.

Now Mum is in school awaiting the Head,
The interview planned for 2.10;
The year tutor's started speaking with her
And going through past crimes again.

Mum doesn't care what Barbara wrote
In her maths book way back in December,
She wants the Head (who is out by the
    gate . . .
And there's no chance that he will
    remember).

They get distracted by Darren and Wayne
Who are fighting for Debbie's attention;
The deputy Head comes out of his room,
Gives those still in sight a detention.

That doesn't include Darren and Wayne
Who have heard there's a fight by the gate.
And Barbara's mum is conversing with Trace
Who's explaining why parties run late.

The vending machine is now charging half
   price
As if it's a closing-down sale.
Tracey has got well into her stride
And Barbara's mum has gone pale.

The caretaker wanders down to the gate,
His Alsatian lolloping after,
Arrives to see handcuffs placed on the Head
And Darren Jones helpless with laughter.

Tina's spray-painting the toilet again,
Barbara's mum's had a turn,
The caretaker sighs and picks up a can:
It's still the first day of term.

Prove It

I love you.

HOW MUCH?

I love you more than Sheena Wilkins, Betty Carmichael and that blonde girl who gets on the bus every morning by the 'Pic'.

THE ONE WHO SITS AT THE BACK?

That's right, the one with the big smile.

BETTER BUT . . .

I love you more than Sheena Wilkins, Betty Carmichael, the blonde on the bus and Debbie Johnson.

SHE'S GOT SPOTS.

Ah, but she gives you Mars bars that she
pinches from her uncle's cash and carry.

WELL I'M NOT SURE . . .

I love you more than Sheena Wilkins, Betty
Carmichael, Debbie Johnson, the blonde
on the bus and the new French teacher
that the headmaster is always popping in to
see.

WHAT'S HER NAME?

Who cares what her name is? Anyway, I said I
love you more than her and, if I love you
more than her, I must love you more than
anyone anywhere . . . ever.

ALL RIGHT.

Now can I borrow your pencil sharpener?

Swimming Lesson (for some)

Jodie doesn't bring her kit,
Sarah brings a letter,
Suzi's wart between her toes
Isn't getting better,
Angela has a cold
Which seems to last forever.
I wouldn't mind the swimming class
If we went in together . . .
>   But we don't
>   There was me
>   And fourteen boys on Tuesday.
>   I hated it.

Marlon called me matchstick legs,
Got the others going,
Craig said I'm a beanstalk
And that's why I keep growing,
Andy's named me skeleton,
Claimed I'm anorexic:
Just because I've got no note
I'm the one who gets it.
>   And the teacher doesn't help
>   She's so terrified that
>   Someone will do something
>   Dangerous
>   She doesn't hear a word
>   Of what they say.

Jodie may come last in maths,
She's first-rate at excuses,
Sarah forges notes that have
Twenty different uses,
Angi's cold and Suzi's wart
Are both their own inventions
And still it's me ('cause I hit Craig)
Who lands up with detentions.
    Why should the one person
    Who doesn't fiddle out of lessons
    Be the one person
    Left here after school?
    Miss gave me
    Twenty-four hours' notice:
    That's more than they'll get
    Next Tuesday.

A Teacher's Head

In it is a mark book
a constantly ticking assessment machine

In it is a pile of books, a mile high
and a bucket of red ink, ready for duty

In it is a bin-ful of absence notes
part-true, part-fiction, part-forgery

In it is more knowledge than is useful
more than any class can comprehend

In it is the perfect lesson, never taught
waiting for the perfect class, never yet

In it is a summer holiday
that lasts from New Year's Day to Christmas

In it is the first day of retirement
and a suspicion of loneliness

'WILL YOU MISS US, MISS?'

Best Kept Out of Sight

Kevin used to be a laugh,
Kev was my best mate,
Kevin had the kind of smirk
That all the teachers hate.

Kevin didn't care too much
For the teachers or the law
'Rules are made to break,' he said,
'And that's what I'm here for.'

In spite of that he did his work
And got good marks as well
Until he told the head of French
That she could go to . . .

     . . . somewhere else
     and it wasn't France,
     it was a good deal further
     than that.

The head of year arranged to see
Him, Tuesday, ten past one.
Kevin didn't fancy that,
Kevin didn't come.

Now Jonesey is our head of year:
You don't mess him about.
He's big, he's hard, he likes his voice
And, my, how he can shout.

No one saw the incident,
In spite of what they say,
So no one knows whose fault it was
To this very day.

Kevin says he went for him,
The staff say that's a lie.
I saw Kevin's swollen lip
And Mr Jones' black eye.

The teachers look sincere and say,
'We couldn't have helped more.
There's always one who tries it on:
That's why there must be law.'

I don't blame them. It's their job.
I only wish they knew
The more they make a fuss of rules,
The more they're tempting you.

Kevin wasn't seen again,
At least, not in our school.
The teachers said it's for the best.
Who do they think they fool?

Kevin was obliged to go
To some place for 'his kind'
Kevin never talked of it.
He said he didn't mind.

I think he did, in spite of that,
Was sorry for the fight.
To schools, he was a problem
Best kept out of sight.

He doesn't tell the jokes these days,
His eyes have lost their grin,
It's awkward and uncomfortable
For me to talk to him.

Kevin had a way with words,
Was brainy, had good taste,
Kev was even good at French.
Isn't that a waste?

Starting High School

Scared as September, standing here,
Like a five-year-old once more:
Clammy palms, sweating arms,
Staring at the floor.

Sick as September, shuffling in
To this aircraft hangar hall:
Lists of rooms, directions, names,
Mine not there at all.

Still as September, there's just me
Left staring at the wall.
Teachers mutter, check the lists:
I don't exist at all.

Safe as September, sitting here,
It's all right on my own.
I've learnt a lot in half an hour,
I think I'm going home.

Daily School Recipe

Take one very loud bell system
And make it ring every forty minutes.
Train pupils to push chairs anywhere.
Arrange the teacher's shout of
'Come back at once'
To sprinkle the air
At the very moment that the last foot
Disappears from view.

When the ingredients are
Settled into another classroom,
Leave for five minutes
To allow it all to ferment.
The mixture is ready
For the addition of a teacher
When the sound of flying books,
Breaking glass or screaming victims
Can be heard
From a distance of at least
Half a corridor.

Season with warnings, threats
And just a pinch of detention
Before placing in front of
A hot blackboard for thirty minutes.
Temperatures and cooking times
Will need to be adjusted
According to manufacturer's instructions
If using a fan-assisted overhead projector.

The dish is ready
When several pens have run out
Or several pupils have fallen asleep.
If overcooked,
There is a tendency for the flavour
To be spoilt by the taste
Of writer's cramp or sprained wrists.

Best served with magazines
Hidden below desk height
Or a crisp cartoon
Of a teacher's exploding brain.

Metalmouth

They promised me:
These would be the happiest days of my life,
School will be such fun, they said.

> Parents forget what happens in
>   playgrounds,
> Parents forget just what it was like,
> Parents are strong on subjects like
>   homework,
> Weak on what to do in a fight.

The teachers said
It was just a matter of settling in,
I'd soon get used to it, they said.

> Teachers forget what happens between
>   rooms,
> Teachers forget just why people skive,
> Teachers are strong on tests and revision,
> Weak on what to do to survive.

Oh, it wasn't too bad.
They called me Metalmouth,
Laughed at the brace on my teeth,
But they didn't hit me.

Teachers forget the power of nicknames,
Parents forget it's hard to be strong,
Everyone's clear on what is expected,
Vague on what to do to belong.

It wasn't as bad
As my cousin tried to terrify me
Into thinking it was
But it isn't the place
They believe it to be . . . not at all.

From Septimus to Smith

The Arrival of Kissing

We'd never heard of kissing
Until Uncle Septimus returned from abroad.
Call us old-fashioned,
Call us out of touch,
It had never occurred to us.

Uncle Septimus came home full of it.
Not full of kisses, you understand,
Full of the idea of kissing,
Although I think he had been practising:
He kept smiling in a lop-sided way
Like a well-worn teddy bear.

'Well you must tell us about it,'
Said my aunt
Who soon wished she hadn't
But with Uncle Septimus
You never know it's too late
Until it is too late
And then you spend hours
Wishing it wasn't
When it is.

Not that I minded.
It amused me:
All these years we've been holding hands
And others,
A mere ship's journey away,
Have been placing their lips
Right up against each other
And making extraordinary sounds.

Aunt Madge said, quite understandably,
That it would have put her off marriage
For life
If any young man
Had ever come up
And tried to interfere with her face
Using his sticky lips.

Uncle Septimus, quite understandably,
Pointed out
That she wasn't married anyway.
'A good job, too,' said Aunt Madge,
'And anyway, what on earth
Accompanies this revolting spectacle?
There must be more to it
Than meets the eye.'

'They close their eyes,' said Uncle.
'Quite the best thing to do,' said Aunt.
'They hold each other tight,' said Uncle.
'Out of sheer horror I expect,' said Aunt.
'And then their tongues . . .'
'That is quite enough
Of your vile ideas,' said Aunt Madge.
'I can see that you've made the whole thing up
To earn free drinks
Off unsuspecting fools in local bars,
We don't want to hear another word.'

But I did, oh, I did.

Mr Smith's Collection

I see you, taking it slowly,
The five dozen yards to the shop,
A brief hallo, a nod, no smile,
A long asthmatic stop.

You'd ask for half a cabbage,
Stare blankly straight ahead,
Choose two or three potatoes,
Buy yesterday's cheap bread.

I liked you Mr Smith.
That's something you wouldn't know.
I would smile but keep on playing,
Mum might say hello.

I never went inside your house,
Dusty, dark, smelling strange.
Time had let it stand apart,
Unmoved, unmarked by change.

You can't have relished life at all,
That last unchanging year,
Regular and solitary,
No friends or family near.

My mother told me you had 'gone'.
She made it sound quite planned.
I asked her to explain. She said
I wouldn't understand.

I understand what happened next:
They stripped your private corners,
Went through the house's secrets
Like vultures more than mourners.

They can not harm you, Mr Smith,
That's the best of being 'gone'.
Did you ever know or guess though
What they would light upon?

The china, so my father says,
Is beautiful and rare.
I'm sorry that I never saw it
When you were living there.

I'm sorry, too, you kept it hid.
'A waste,' my mother said.
A shame, too, when I think you bought
Yesterday's cheap bread.

If you were still alive, mind,
If only for a while,
I wouldn't want to just see plates
I'd want to see you smile.

Selling a Table

A quiet night, the others out,
A single knock upon the door,
A cautious wary opening,
A lined face, never seen before.

He said he'd come to see the table,
Seen the advert, liked the sound.
No warning: he just arrived
Like frost upon the winter ground.

I stood uncertain, insecure,
Not wanting to invite him in;
A prickling cold ran down my back
Like spider paths upon the skin.

I had no choice, no good excuse,
I let him in, chose not to smile;
He took his time, he didn't buy,
Muttered about size and style.

He turned and faced me suddenly,
I looked for gun or fist or knife.
Instead he talked about his house,
His dog, his gardening, his life.

When he left, I felt ashamed
Of my suspicious fear.
A loneliness had knocked my door:
I'd chose not to hear.

Old Woman in the Park

You will see me,
Sitting like the remnants of a jumble sale,
On the third bench, left-hand side,
As you come into the park.

I am not a witch,
I am not unpleasant to smell,
And I am not sitting here so that young
    people,
Skipping school,
Can laugh at me and jeer at me.

I am old, I am poor
And, yes, I am embarrassed:
That is the worst of it.
There should be no shame
In poverty or age.
I keep my eyes down,
Stare vacantly at the flowers,
I make sure that I do not catch your eye.

The nice middle-aged people,
Out walking their well-groomed dogs,
See a shuffling sack of clothes,
Heading homeward to her one room,
I want to stop and talk to them,
'Tell them who I am'.

I am the person who they will be
In a short journey from now,
Unless their children can be kinder
Than they are.

Debbie's New Year

This year,
I shall tell my grandmother
Exactly what I think
Of the sensible cardigans
She knits for me.

This year,
When my father goes on about table
   manners
And the family are all eating together
And being grateful for lentil stew
And getting life into perspective,
I shall pick my nose.

This year,
I shall shop like a middle-aged woman
With hard elbows
Designed for queues.

This year,
I shall run the supermarket trolley
Over the toes of
Whoever stares down their nose at me
And, instead of saying,
'I'm dreadfully sorry,'
I shall smirk.

This year,
I shall refuse to stand on the touchlines
Whilst my stupid brother
Gets crushed in a scrum.

This year,
I shall copy my homework
From at least two different books
And so avoid long explanations
As to why Donna and I
Have seventeen identical wrong answers.

This year,
I shall buy chocolate, come what may,
And blame the spots
On the weather
    the stars
    comet dust
    radioactive fall-out
Or whatever happens to be
Scapegoat of the month.

This year,
I shall stop telling the bus driver I'm thirteen
And the club doorman I'm eighteen
And get a boyfriend with a car.

This year,
If all else fails,
I shall borrow my mother's clothes
Cigarettes and curlers
Stick a cushion up the front of my dress
And waddle around the estate
Until somebody notices me.
. . . I will!

Perfectly Peculiar

A Fistful of Pacifists

A thimbleful of giants
A rugby scrum of nuns
An atom of elephants
A cuddle of guns

A rustle of rhinoceros
A barrel of bears
A stampede of tortoises
A bald patch of hairs

A stumble of ballet dancers
A flutter of whales
A mouthful of silence
A whisper of gales

A pocketful of earthquakes
A conference of pears
A fistful of pacifists
A round-up of squares.

Domino Poems

Trees make paper
Paper makes books
Books make learning
Learning makes teachers
Teachers make lessons
Lessons make homework
TREES HAVE A LOT
TO ANSWER FOR

The sun makes warmth
Warmth makes summer
Summer makes holidays
Holidays make love
Love makes promises
Promises make marriage
Marriage makes parents
Parents make rules
THE SUN HAS A LOT
TO ANSWER FOR AS WELL.

The Plug Hole

Some people are really stupid
About plug holes.
They imagine all sorts of things about them.
Hands coming up out of the darkness,
Unspeakable insects grabbing them.
Not me.
Nothing like that bothers me.

THEN WHY ARE YOU STARING
SO HARD AT IT?

Am I?
Well I just like to imagine
What worries other people.
I know that there are
No little people
Living down in the sewer
Waiting to come up the drains
And suck my entrails out.
I'll just put the plug in
And have my bath.

WHY ARE YOU HAMMERING
THAT PLUG INTO POSITION?

Am I?
Well I don't like to lose
Any bath water.
You know what they used to say:
Save water,
Bath with a friend.
Well I don't bath with a friend
But I like to save water.

YOU'RE WAFFLING

Am I?
Well I suppose I ought to get on
And have this bath.
You don't have to go,
I quite like company in the bathroom.
My brother told me once
How blood started seeping around the plug
And into his bath water
And when a drop of it touched his toe
The skin shrivelled and went black.

JUST HAVE YOUR BATH.

Oh, all right.
There we are, nothing to be afraid of
Is there?
In fact, I quite like to relax
In a steaming hot bath
With nothing to bother me.

JUST CLOSE YOUR EYES
AND I'LL DO THE SHAMPOO FOR YOU.

Oh, all right.
Why are your hands going hairy?
You're not wearing gloves are you?
And why are those teeth
Glinting like that?
I'd swear they were growing
long . . . . a a a a a agh!

Hot Air

Rhubarb, rubbish,
balderdash, blether,

Hokum, bunkum,
baloney, bosh,

Gabbling, jabber,
gibberish, babble,

Patter, piffle, poppycock,
Bilge, bilge, bilge,

Claptrap, flimflam,
flummery, flannel,

Waffle, twaddle,
tommyrot, tripe,

Small talk, chin-wag,
yatter break, prattle,

Natter, drivel, gossip club,
Gas, gas, gas.

Elementary Human Cookery

Try eating boys up for breakfast,
Gobbling a girlfriend for lunch.
Fillet of friend with a sisterly sauce
Makes a mouth-watering munch.

First forms are better pan-fried or grilled:
Their delicate flavours will thrive.
Sixth forms braise well in a medium heat
But teachers need boiling alive.

The younger the meat, the quicker it cooks,
The more pleasure that eating will be.
Parents are better pot roasted or baked
To one of their own recipes.

Sausages made out of neighbours,
Enemies chopped into stew:
Always enjoy the dish of the day . . .
Tomorrow we casserole you.

U Knee Verse

A   stacks are good to sleep in
B   troot sandwiches are yuck
C   d looking bloke
D   sent looking bloke
E   did it, not me
F   only I hadn't got caught
G   knee us
H   l o is larger than a violin
I   for an i
J   l him for life
K   tering for all tastes
L   bow grease
M   barrassed by my spots
N   joyed the party
O   pless at spellin
P   pol keep staring at me
Q   er ring my bad habits is impossible
R   you sure it was him
S   a was due in yesterday
T   tering on the brink
U   knee verse
V   nus and Mars bars
W   up with pain
X   hausted by trying to work this out
Y   me
Z   too much and had to sit in silence.

Thin Ice

You never know where
                                        you
            are
with poems.
Just as you think
you've got the meanings
            all
            neatly   s   out of line s
                              p   c
            sorted   m   a
                         u   t
some word or j   t
    phrase   e
                                                             r
                                                             i
                                                             n
                                                             g

all your well-arranged thoughts.

You're flying without instruments,
    leaping without parachutes,
      skating on thin ice,
with someone always hoping
that you'll   f
              a
                l
                  l
                    i
                      n

Specimen

And this is our rarest specimen of all:
The last living human.
Oh, you can see their bones in museums,
I know that,
But you will be one of the last of our
    community
To see one alive.

Yes, there were millions of them once.
I've heard my grandfather speak of
Hunting them for sport,
A fine sport, too,
And fair;
Never more than six wolves to the hunt
So the human had a chance.

Cruel?
I don't think so.
They were hunters themselves, you know.
Our history says that
As the size of their weapons increased
The size of their brains got smaller.

No, personally, I don't believe that.
There's another theory that one of their
    weapons

Caused horrible changes,
Killed many of them and left their children
And their children's children different,
Helpless.

The history books find that too fanciful
But I wouldn't be too sure.

Oh, it has to be behind those bars
For its safety
And it certainly wouldn't survive
In the wild, anymore.
It's kindness really and,
Being a dumb human,
It doesn't really understand its situation.

The eyes?
Oh, the eyes often water like that.
It's part of the cleansing mechanism
For its vision.
Very effective, I believe,
But of no further significance.

Sad?
Well, yes I suppose it is
But that's progress, isn't it?

Dreams of an Everyday Dustbin

I'd rather be a dustbin
Than a human.
Dustbins get attention
Once a week, without fail,
And a decent swill of disinfectant
If they smell.
No work in being a dustbin:
You just sit there and open wide.
You don't even get messy like you used to.
Tidy black plastic bags
Keep your insides neat.
No fear of the dole queue, either;
Everyone wants a dustbin,
Even posh houses
With waste disposal units,
Though it's more for show with them
Than an absolute necessity.
Of course there are problems:
Lolloping great hounds, for example,
Who knock you over
And go through all your bits.
But, notice, it's the dog who gets the blame
For its ill-mannered greed
Not the dustbin
With its carelessly fitted lid.
Oh, you get away with murder
If you're a dustbin.

It's a grand outdoor life
And it keeps you healthy:
Dustbins never get colds
Or sore throats or back-ache,
Dustbins never have to worry
About where the next meal is coming from,
Dustbins even get through Christmas
With nothing worse than a few turkey bones
Sticking in their side.
Others can dream of fortune and fame,
Others can dream of glory and honour,
I dream about being a dustbin.

Blunt Words

Blunt words
One sound words
Like NO
Or WAIT
Or STOP

They stalk me
Fence me in
NOT NOW
NOT YET
NEXT YEAR

Hard words
One thought words
Like GO
Or WORK
Or YOU

They cut me
Ask too much
Like WIN
Or PASS
Or FIRST

I need the words
With several syllables
Like perhaps
Or possibly
Or however
Words to soften
The definitions
And the demands

I need phrases
With a breathing space in them
Like 'in a little while'
Or 'whatever you can'
Or 'within reason'

I want words
That make space for me
Kinder words
Phrases with potential
Sentences that
Give me a chance

Now That You've Passed . . .

Can grate you lessons

Can grant your lay sums

Can graft your lichens

Can grunt your life signs

Can conk your left shins

King Kong your leg shines

Kong King your loft stuns

Can groan your late sins

Con gran you lend sons

Con grab relations

Congra . . .

WELL DONE.

Never Play Leapfrog with a Unicorn

Never play leapfrog
with a unicorn.

Never tap dance
with an elephant.

Don't let your bicycle
start an argument
with a ten ton truck.

A friend in need
is usually in debt.

Once bitten, you watch
your baby brother's
teeth more carefully.

Never let a python
have a crush on you.

Never arm wrestle
an octopus.

Perfectly Normal

Got a ticket to exhibit
My plans to change forever
Got a licence to do brain swaps
And a pen to change the weather

Got a visa for a freezer
Where I ice up politicians
Got petitions from the voters
Supporting my decisions

Got a mandate to develop
My research on mind extension
Got a patent for my helmet
That prevents thought intervention

Got a seat on the committee
Which allocates ice creams
Got a letter from the Yeti
Interpreting my dreams

Got a ticket, got a permit
Got a licence, got a letter . . .
Got prescriptions from my doctor
So I must be getting better!

Say What You Think

Sexes: a poem for two voices

Why do girls change their mind without
  warning?
Why do boys change their socks once a year?
Why do girls make a fuss about spiders?
Why do boys shout and drink too much beer?

Why do girls meet you outside the venue
And leave you to freeze when they're late?
Why do boys eat like pigs at a trough
With their noses an inch from the plate?

Why do girls have to dance around handbags
Or go to the toilet in pairs?
And why do they tell you that everything's
  fine
Then suddenly burst into tears?

Why do boys clean their shoes on their jeans
Or pretend that they never get cold
And why forget what they shoved in the
  fridge
Until it's half-covered in mould?

Why do girls do their homework on time
And why collect things they don't use?
Why do boys wear rude slogans on T-shirts
Or get into fights when in queues?

Why do girls diet but still eat cream cakes?
Why do boys run home to mother?
And why, when it's clear that they can't get
    along,
Do the sexes still fancy each other?

Poisoning People is Wrong

You've done it again haven't you?
You've eaten the cherries
And given the rest of your cake to the rabbit.

I SAY NOTHING.

And who gave the crust of the pork pie
To the dog?
Who?
I'll bet it was you.
He's been sick twice this morning you know.

ALL THE MORE REASON
FOR ME NOT TO EAT IT.

I keep finding crusts all over the house.
You're supposed to eat the whole of the
　　bread
Not shove the bits you don't like in your
　　pocket
And stick them in the bookcase later on.
I'd sniffed my way around
Fourteen Dickens novels
Before I found your rotten crusts.
They'd gone green.
Are you listening?
Green, they'd gone.

SO SHE'S DESTROYED MY PENICILLIN
   FACTORY.
SHE HATES SCIENTISTS.

As for that cabbage.
If you'd said you didn't want it
I wouldn't have given you so much.
You're disgusting you are.

WELL SOMETHING WAS NEEDED
TO FILL THAT GAP AT THE
BACK OF THE SOFA.

Baked potatoes
Are meant to be eaten,
Not be poked about.
And don't leave the skin this time:
That's the bit with all the vitamins.

THAT'S ALSO THE BIT WITH
ALL THE MUD IF SHE'S LEFT
MY FATHER TO SCRUB THEM.

Yes, we are having rice pudding for afters
And, yes, you do have to eat it.
In my day
You were grateful if you got rice pudding.
In my day
Things were different.

IN HER DAY IT WAS ILLEGAL TO POISON
CHILDREN.

Are you muttering something?

ME? NOT ME.

Not That Funny

Hey, you,
Yes, you.
Not me?
Yes, you.
Why me?
We're through.
What you and me?
Yes, us.
Why us?
Because I was . . .
Go on.
I was the one.
Which one?
The one
Made fun of
By your friends.
Our friends?
Your friends,
Not mine,
They laughed behind
My back and . . .
And what?
And you.
Yes, what?
You laughed too.

We Are Not Having an Argument

WHY DO YOU AND DAD ARGUE
ABOUT WHO SHOULD PUT THE CAT
OUT?
We don't argue about it.
Sometimes your father forgets
That it's his turn
And we have a discussion
Concerning his memory.

WHY DO YOU DISCUSS HIS MEMORY
BY SHOUTING?
Because your father was brought up
Without the faintest idea
About how educated people
Can solve their problems
In a quiet and self-controlled manner.

IS THAT BECAUSE
HE WAS BORN IN A BARN?
When I say that your father
Was born in a barn,
I am merely referring to his
Total and complete failure
Ever to close any door behind him
Which is a typical example
Of male idleness and selfishness.

**WHY DO YOU SAY
HE WAS BORN IN A BARN,
IF HE WASN'T BORN IN A BARN?**
It's an expression which adults use
To show disapproval
Of an individual's failure
To close a door behind them.
It does not mean that they were
Literally born in a barn.

WHERE WAS HE BORN THEN?
Your father was born in
Macclesfield Road Maternity Unit
Which is a mile down the road
From where your nanna lives

IS IT A BARN?
Of course it's not a barn,
It's a maternity unit.
I've just explained to you
That when we say
Someone was born in a barn
They don't actually have to be
Literally born in a literal barn.

WHAT'S A LITERAL BARN?
I am not going to lose my temper
I am going to deal with you
In the same calm manner
I deal with your father
If you say another word
I shall simply engage in
Reasonable physical restraint.

WHAT'S REAS . . .?

OUCH!

This

What's this?
What, miss?
Look: this!
Oh that,
That's mine.
It's fine,
It doesn't bite.
It might.
It did.
Did what?
It got
Too hot
And bit
A bit
Of it.
Of what?
Of what
It got.
Well, miss,
See this.
That's it:
The bit.

Going Out

Me mum is putting warpaint on,
Me dad is hunting socks,
Me auntie's come to baby-sit
And she's glued to the box.

I heard them in the bedroom . . .
Including all the language.
A zip has caught her skin again,
He's gone for a bandage.

Me mum has got the legs and arms
You need to do karate
And, yet, I'll bet her dress will be
The shortest at the party.

Listen to them arguing
About the driving rota:
An hour from now I wouldn't trust them
Even near the motor.

'Have you got the keys, dear?'
'Does that seam need mending?'
My estimate is they'll arrive
Just as the party's ending.

Me mum will blame it all on Dad,
He'll live on excuses.
There may be jobs that parents do;
I've yet to find their uses.

Me mum is irresponsible,
Me dad's the same and boring.
It's good I'm here to mind the house:
The baby-sitter's snoring.

First Steps in Healthy Eating

The eggs that you eat should be free range,
Battery hens are so wrong.
Cooped up in cages with no room to move:
That's not where the creatures belong.

Give them the freedom to roam as they wish,
Keep additives out of their food,
Don't let them end up as chicken chasseur.
How would you like to be chewed?

Vegetables should be organic,
That's really the only safe way.
The rest will be normally poisoned
By doses of pesticide spray.

Rump steak is out – it's the hormones
They use for enhancing the meat.
Although the best beef may look leaner,
How many want hormones to eat?

Before you eat fish from our coastline,
Read the offshore sewage report.
If they eat a fraction of what we have dumped,
They're hardly food for thought.

Sodium nitrate, E.102,
Uranium, mercury, lead,
Antibiotics, insecticides:
The puzzle is why we're not dead.

Habits must change and, just for a start,
We really should cut out the worst:
With sea salt and jacket potatoes,
Eat food manufacturers first.

Dress Sense

You're not going out in that, are you?
I've never seen anything
More ridiculous in my whole life.
You look like you've been dragged
Through a hedge backwards
And lost half your dress along the way.

What's *wrong* with it?
You're asking me what's wrong with *that*?
Everything: that's what.
It's loud, it's common,
It reveals far too much of your . . .
Your . . . well your 'what you shouldn't be
    revealing'.

No I'm not going to explain;
You know very well what I mean, young lady
But you choose to ignore
Every single piece of reasonable helpful advice
That you are offered.

It's not just the neckline I'm talking about
And you can hardly describe it as a neckline,
More like a navel-line
If you bother to observe the way that it
    plunges.
Have you taken a look at the back?
(What little there is of it.)

Have you?
Boys are only going to think
One thing
When they see you in that outfit.
Where on earth did you get it?
And don't tell me that my money paid for it
Whatever you do.

You found it *where*?

Well it probably looked different on her
And, anyway, you shouldn't be going through
Your mother's old clothes.

Gerbils, Gardens and Grans

High Time You Grew Up

Just because they've turned the lights off
Doesn't mean there's anything out there.
They always turn them out when they go to
    bed,
That's normal.
Anyway I'm supposed to be asleep.

What's that noise?
Behind the wardrobe . . .
A tiny shuffling,
A mouse.

So what?
They're sweet grey furry things.

Not when the whole bedroom floor
Is covered with them
And they're hungry
And one or two have started
Jumping at the side of my bed.
MUM!

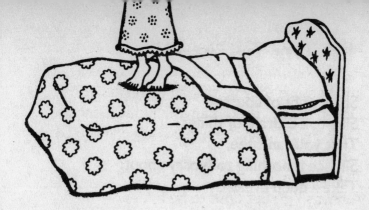

A thump,
A heavy thud, thud,
A light on,

GO TO SLEEP.
But Mum!
YOUR FATHER HAS PUT ENOUGH
MOUSE POISON DOWN TO KILL
THE POPULATION OF LONDON.

AND BIRMINGHAM.
BUT.
NO BUTS.

Four steps, switch, two steps,
A long sigh,
A creak of springs.

She's right of course
Silly to be afraid of things
That you can't see,
Silence is nothing to worry about.
Take a deep breath.

What was that?
Get a grip on yourself,
That's just a branch
Brushing against the window.
It can't be a burglar
'Cause we've got nothing worth burgling.

Then it's the man with black eyes
And black fingernails
Who waits until you're asleep
Creeps in
And scratches up a bit of your skin
And, when he's got under your skin,
He slowly starts peeling it back
Inch by inch
Rolling it up until he comes to . . .
DAD!

Several heavy thumps,
A word I can't quite hear

DON'T TELL ME,
DON'T START
KEEP YOUR ****LIGHT ON
Thanks

HOW OLD ARE YOU?
Thirty-four next birthday, Dad.

The Purse

I pinched it from my mother's purse,
Pretending it's a game.
My muscles tightened: hard and tense.
I pinched it just the same.

'I need it as a loan,' I said,
'It's not against the law.'
'I won't do it again,' I said.
I've said all that before.

The reason was the cash at first,
It isn't anymore;
I do it . . . well, because I do,
I don't know what it's for.

I only know that when the house
Is silent, empty, still,
I head towards my parents' room
As if against my will.

The sweat is cold upon my neck,
My back and arms feel strange,
I'm sure that someone's watching me
As I pick out her change.

But no one ever catches me,
Sometimes I wish they would;
Then perhaps I'd stop and think
And give it up for good.

But my mum trusts me, buys me things:
Each kindness makes it worse
Because I know, when she's next door,
My hands will find her purse.

Box of Gerbils

I'm fast awake,
I'm wide asleep,
I've got a box of gerbils
I'm not allowed to keep;
I'd give them to my sister
But she would go berserk,
I'd keep them in the video
If I thought that it would work;
I'd give them to my uncle,
Who's working as a driver
But he'd paint them funny colours
And sell them for a fiver;
I'd lend them all to Tony
Who kept frogs in his attic
But his mother found them last week
And went a bit dramatic;
I'd give them to my brother
'Cause he hasn't got a pet
But he's told me what he's planning
With his 'Fun and Science' set.
I'm wide asleep,
I'm fast awake,
It's coming up for school time
So I'll do the stomach-ache.

I'm fast awake,
I'm wide asleep,
I've still got twenty gerbils
I'm not allowed to keep;
I've only got an hour left
To re-locate my pets
Or my father says he'll take
The whole lot down the vet's;
And the vet, he smiles nicely
But I know just what he'll do
'Cause his family are famous
For eating gerbil stew.
So I'm getting in a panic,
Trying this and that,
Though I'm sorry that I stuck three
Inside Grandad's hat.
It didn't make them safer,
I forgot they'd need a snack
And when they nibbled Grandad
He promptly bit them back.
I'm wide asleep,
I'm fast awake,
I'm running out of time and
I've twenty friends at stake.

I'm fast awake,
I'm wide asleep,
My father's got the box now,
He's a gerbil-hating creep;
He said it's best for everyone
And talked about infection:
He sounds just like the doctor
When she's planning an injection.
She and him should write a book
With their assembled brain
Called *Twenty Thousand Reasons
For Giving People Pain.*
There isn't any hope now,
There's nothing to discuss,
They were all right in my sister's bed
But she made a fuss;
I thought Dad might see sense
If he grew a little calmer:
A shame about the gerbil
I'd stuffed up his pyjama.
I'm wide asleep,
I'm fast awake,
They've taken all my gerbils . . .
But they haven't found the snake.

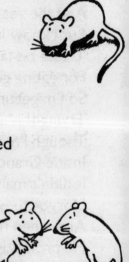

Message on the Table:
an acrostic poem

Your dinner is in the
Oven because I'm taking
Uncle
Jack
Up to your grandmother's.
She hasn't seen him in years.
There's also extra sauce in
A pan on the stove. It needs
To be warmed through
Even if you manage to get in on time.
Wash up and
Open a can of something if you're still
Ravenous, although you
May not be if you work out my
Secret.

The Garden, Explained

WHY IS THE GRASS GREEN?
That's because it doesn't have flowers.
When it looks at the snowdrops
And the crocuses and the daffodils,
It knows it will never have colours like that
So it turns green with envy.

WELL, WHY IS SKY BLUE?
It doesn't want to be
Confused with the grass.

AND WHY DO ROSES SMELL NICE?
That's to hide the manure
Your grandad dumps on their feet.

AND WHY DOES GRANDPA
GROW HIS ROSES IN OUR GARDEN?
Because your father
Is too busy writing down nonsense
Like this
When he could be doing something useful.